Giselle

GISELLE

or THE WILIS

Adapted from
    Théophile Gautier

by VIOLETTE VERDY

Illustrated by
    Marcia Brown

McGraw-Hill Book Company

NEW YORK   ST. LOUIS   SAN FRANCISCO   DUSSELDORF
LONDON   MEXICO   PANAMA   SYDNEY   TORONTO

To the dancers who have made *Giselle* live

Text copyright © 1970 by Violette Verdy and illustrations copyright © 1970 by
Marcia Brown. All Rights Reserved. Printed in the United States of America. No
part of this publication may be reproduced, stored in a retrieval system, or trans-
mitted, in any form or by any means, electronic, mechanical, photocopying, record-
ing, or otherwise, without the prior written permission of the publisher.
Library of Congress Catalog Card Number: 74-107299
1234567890 MUEC 7876543210

Foreword

The ballet of *Giselle* was first performed in Paris, in 1841. The scenario, by the poet Théophile Gautier and the librettist Jules de Saint-Georges, was based on a folk tradition mentioned in the writings of the German poet H. Heine. The ballet, with choreography by Coralli and music by Adolphe Adam, was an instant success. Shortly before the premiere, Gautier acknowledged his debt to Heine in a charming open letter. In a later article, Gautier described *Giselle* in full detail for the benefit of the reading public. The following text is an adaptation of that article. The original French text may be found in Gautier's *Les Beautés de L'Opéra*, a collection of writings covering twenty-five years of theater life in Paris.

My dear Henri Heine, while leafing through your beautiful book,
de l'Allemagne, a few weeks ago, I came across a charming
passage (one has merely to open the volume at random). It
was the passage in which you speak of white-robed elves
whose hems are always damp, of water nymphs who leave
traces of their little satin feet on the ceiling of the nuptial
chamber, of wilis as pale as snow, those unpitying waltzers,
and of all the delicious apparitions that you have met in the
Hartz mountains and on the banks of the Ilse in the velvety
mist of German moonlight—and I said out loud, "What a
pretty ballet one might make of that!"

In a rush of enthusiasm, I even took a large, lovely sheet of white paper and wrote at the top, in a superbly clear script: LES WILIS, ballet. Then I burst out laughing and threw the paper away without going any further, telling myself that it was certainly impossible to translate all of that into theatrical terms—that misty nocturnal poetry, that voluptuously sinister phantom world, all those effects of legend and ballad that have so little in common with our customs. That evening at the Opera, my head still full of your ideas, I met at the turning of a corridor the man of wit who, by adding so much of his own, knew how to infuse a ballet with all the fantasy and all the caprice of Le Diable Amoureux by Cazotte, the great poet who invented Hoffmann in the middle of the eighteenth century, according to the complete Encyclopedia. I told him the legend of the wilis. Three days later, the ballet of Giselle was finished and accepted. At the end of the week, Adolphe Adam had composed the music, the scenery was nearly completed, and rehearsals went into full swing....

GISELLE

ACT I

*A*s the curtain rises you see, gilded by a warm shaft of sun-
light, a steep bank of the Rhine in all the magnificence of its autumn
dress. It is almost time for the vintage: the amber grapes are swell-
ing beneath their leaves of russet and saffron. And in the depths
of the valley flows the river Rhine.

9

A cottage, humble but charming, nestles in a corner, tucked away like a bird's nest among the vines and foliage. Opposite lies a small hut. And off in the distance, perched on the crest of a rock, shine the white pepperbox turrets of a lofty feudal retreat, one of

those frowning fortresses from whose heights the nobles, like so many vultures, would sweep down to prey on poor travelers.

From that castle—with gentler intentions by far—has come young Count Albrecht, a handsome lad of courtly bearing. From

the heights of his rock, the hawk has seen the dove fluttering in the plain. That dove is Giselle, a charming girl, the daughter of Berthe.

Now you might well imagine that knightly spurs, the arms of a nobleman, and a fine doublet of delicate fur would frighten away the modest Giselle. Even a simple girl knows that counts do not marry peasants—not even in the world of ballet. Albrecht knows it too. He has therefore come disguised as a young villager; only his courtly manners hint at his noble origin. He sends his squire Wilfred back to the castle while he himself remains behind in the hut facing Giselle's cottage, awaiting the greatest happiness a man can experience, especially if he is rich and powerful: the happiness of being loved for himself.

Daylight is breaking. The cottage door opens a little and Giselle darts forth, nimble and joyous as only the pure-hearted can be. Now what would a young girl think of first, when rising in the early morning, all in the red flush and fragrance of dawn? Would she take a basket and sickle and run off to the vineyard? Those who would say "yes" know but little of a maiden's heart.

No indeed! Giselle senses the presence of her love. He is there, alert and ready to dance. So at the risk of brushing the dew off a few flowers, she, too, is going to dance a little. That is only fair; she has not danced since yesterday—a whole long night spent between the cold sheets, without music, and with one's feet absolutely still—heavens! how much time has been lost!

For Giselle has one fault—at least that is what her mother calls
it. She is mad about the dance; she dreams only of dances under
green arbors, of endless waltzes, and of waltzers who never weary.
Albrecht, known to Giselle only as Loys, is undoubtedly the per-
fect partner for her. He never interrupts the dancing with, "It is
too hot, let us rest!" Loys is always ready to dance on and Giselle

loves him with all the devotion of her warm heart. Indeed, what maiden would not be taken with a young gallant who never misses the beat, who never gets dizzy, and whose hands—unlike those of the village boys—are as white as if he had never done a day's work?

Yes, Loys is a fine dancer, but does he love as well as he dances? Young men today are so deceitful!

Flowers are more truthful. Here is a pretty daisy with a golden heart encircled by a wreath of silver, whose every petal, like a little tongue, knows how to spell a word in the book of the future—the future of lovers, of course.

Giselle picks the daisy. How her hand trembles as she plucks fearfully at the frail petals! *He loves me—a little, passionately, not*

at all! Not at all! answers the wretched flower and Giselle throws
it to the ground in despair. But Albrecht (or Loys, if you prefer)
retrieves the offending daisy and corrects the oracle: *He loves me
—he loves me—he loves—loves—loves.* A good-looking young
man can always make the flowers do his bidding.

Giselle is reassured. The cloud of sadness lifts, and laughter,
that pink flower of the soul, brightens her fresh features once again.

Joining her friends, she goes off to the vintage—much to the satis-
faction of Mother Berthe.

So far all has gone well; but of all the good things in this life, the
one most begrudged is happiness. People may forgive the rich for
being rich, the powerful for being powerful, and the famous for
being famous; but the happy are never forgiven.

A jealous eye is watching Giselle. Hilarion, a rough and mysterious gamekeeper straight out of an old German ballad, yearns
for her with a love that borders on hatred, a love that consumes

those twisted hearts who know they can never be loved in return. It is a love turned to bitterness.

Hilarion knows that Loys, far from being a peasant, is really a young lord of high and noble lineage, and that he is moreover betrothed to the fair Princess Bathilde. After breaking into Loys's hut through an open window, he has found the proof: the knightly sword, the spurs, and the emblazoned cloak.

With a word he can kill Giselle.

But see! The grapes have all been gathered. The villagers return
with brimming baskets, ready to celebrate. Giselle, crowned with
vine leaves and carried triumphantly aloft, is proclaimed the new

Queen of the Vintage. A rustic festival! What a splendid occasion
for dancing. Everyone joins in, and above all Giselle, whose little
feet cannot keep still.

"Wretched child," pleads Mother Berthe, "you will dance to your death! And when you die, you will become a *wili*. You will go to the midnight ball in a dress of moonlight, with bracelets of dew clinging to your cold, white arms. You will draw the travelers into a fatal round and then hurl them, all panting and streaming with sweat, into the icy waters of the lake. You will become a vampire of the dance!"

But Giselle answers these motherly chidings much as any daughter would when reminded by her mother that the hour is late: "I am not weary—one more little *contredanse*—only one more!"

For Berthe's child is an incurable
dancer and not at all alarmed at
her mother's warnings.

What of it?
To dance on after death—
would that be so frightening?
Is it then such a pleasure to lie stiff and still
between six planks and two small boards?

Moreover, when a girl is pretty, young, and in love, how can
she believe in death?

Halloo! The shrill flourish of hunting horns echoes through the valley, followed by the barking of hounds straining at the huntsmen's leash. Horses prance and rear. It is the brilliant retinue of Princess Bathilde, out hunting with the Duke, her father.

Loys barely has time to slip away unnoticed.

The hunt has made the Princess weary and thirsty. She seeks a place to rest and taste the sweet milk and the fresh brown country

bread that princesses fancy. And, it happens, she is standing right
in front of Giselle's cottage.

Mother Berthe appears with a great many curtsies, hand in hand
with her daughter, who is ashamed to be caught thus unprepared
for a visit by so great a lady. But the Princess seems so kind that
one can almost forget how beautiful and noble she is, and how rich
and powerful.

After having served Bathilde, the little village girl approaches
her furtively. With the curiosity of a little cat, she stretches her
hand toward the Princess and, as if by chance, strokes the rich,
heavy fabric of her gown.

Bathilde, who has noticed the ruse, laughs with all the good
humor of a great lady and places a long, finely wrought necklace
of gold about Giselle's neck. Then she kisses the pretty peasant
girl. Poor Giselle, flushed with pleasure and embarrassment, does
not suspect that the proud Princess, swathed in velvet and jewels,
is her rival; but it is so. The fatal truth is about to be disclosed in
all its terrible light. For here comes that troublemaker, Hilarion.

May the devil take him, in his buckskin boots, his wolfskin cap, and his green jerkin!

He fetches Count Albrecht's cloak, spurs, and sword; Loys, returning all too soon, finds himself unmasked before Bathilde and the nobles.

Alas, sweet Giselle, your love was not what he seemed. A deadly chill seizes your heart, for great lords do not marry peasants. Besides, there stands Princess Bathilde, motionless in her surprise, and you cannot help but see her beauty.

A maiden's reason lies in her heart. When that heart is wounded, her reason falters.

Thus it is that Giselle lapses into madness—not the forehead-smiting frenzy of some disheveled heroine of melodrama, but a gentle madness, tender and sweet as Giselle herself. The music of the steps she danced with her beloved Loys, before he was Count Albrecht, comes back to her. She starts to dance, whirling faster and faster.

Suddenly, a flash of reason brings her back to the present. She tries to kill herself by falling on the sword brought by Hilarion. Loys quickly pushes the steely point aside, but it is too late. Giselle is wounded and will never recover. A few faltering steps, and she falls dead in her mother's arms, to the deep despair of Albrecht and even Hilarion, who now senses all the horror of his crime—for it is he who has killed Giselle.

Thus ends the first act.

Giselle has danced her way to death. But what of her repose after death? Who can forget Mother Berthe's sinister predictions and the legend of the wilis? The poor girl, alas, is not fated to sleep quietly in her grassy bed. To die at fifteen after going to scarcely a hundred dances and waltzing a mere two thousand waltzes! How do you expect that those charming little feet, more restless, more quivering than a bird's wings, will be still and not try to unwind the straight folds of the shroud, will not steal out into the moonlight to the glade where the rabbit polishes his whiskers with his paw, where the deer starts up, sniffing the air, his muzzle black and shining, there to frolic in the magic circle traced by the spirits of the night?

It is not life that one regrets leaving behind at fifteen—it is dancing and love, and not being able to leave the grave when one's beloved passes by, or inviting him for the next contredanse.

As for you, dear Albrecht, who never yet refused an invitation to dance, your future seems quite alarming, for it may well end with an icy bath in the waters of the lake or at the very least — double pneumonia.

ACT II

*T*he curtain rises on a mysterious forest, such as one sees in old prints. Tall trees with twisted trunks and tangled branches send their knotty roots plunging like thirsty snakes into the black, stagnant water. The wide leaves of the water lily and lotus unfold on the pond's surface. The tall grasses and ground plants mingle with the water reeds, whose velvety tips quiver in the night breeze.

A bluish mist bathes the spaces between the trees, creating fantastic shapes, the forms and movements of spectres. Are those the silvery trunks of aspens—or the pale shouds of ghosts? And does not the moon's sweet, sad, opal face, peeping through the tattered foliage, recall the transparent whiteness of a consumptive maiden?

The whole forest seems full of tears and sighs. Was it the dew or the rain that hung that pearl of moisture at the tip of that blade of grass? Is it indeed the wind that sobs in the reeds?

Who can tell?

Why is the velvet grass flattened only in certain spots? No human steps have ever ventured this far, nor is it from this bank that the herds of doe and roebuck descend to quench their thirst at the pool. This faint, sweet perfume is not that of wildflowers; the pink-centered bellflower and blue forget-me-not have no such fragrance.

Soon you shall come to the heart of this mystery.

In a corner overgrown by weeds and wildflowers stands a cross of stone, all new and white. A stray moonbeam reveals the name on the cross: GISELLE. It is there that Hilarion's victim lies buried in the cold earth, dead at fifteen.

But what can these bold hunters be doing in such a place? Instead of hare or deer, they will see only phantoms, against whom shot and gunpowder are unavailing.

This spot is haunted by evil, bold companions! Take your venison pie and your brandy flasks elsewhere. Listen! Midnight is striking—the uneasy hour when the living are gathered in and the dead go abroad. The will-o'-the-wisps, glittering butterflies of the night, begin fluttering about you. Scornful folk may laugh at will-o'-the-wisps and say they are caused by marsh gases, but you, worthy hunters, know that the glimmerings are souls in pain or evil spirits.

And you, brutish Hilarion, do not your shaky knees and the icy sweat that glues your hair to your temples, make you realize that you are close to Giselle's grave?

Brave as they are, the hunters take fright and flee. The spot is deserted, and the evening star, opening its silvery eyelids, pours a brighter light onto the clearing. Do you not see there, among the tall weeds, something like a trodden circle, showing the dancing place of the wilis? It is there that they celebrate their magic ball.

Look! The grass quivers, the heart of a four-o'clock unfolds, releasing a white vapor that soon condenses into the shape of a beautiful young girl, pale and cold as moonlight on snow. It is the Queen of the Wilis.

The tip of her wand traces cabalistic circles in the air as she summons her subjects from beyond the four winds. They are all women, these followers of Myrtha, as well they must be; men are too coarse, too stupid, too much in love with their own tough skins to die a romantic death. Their graves would never bear the epitaph:

He loved the dance too much;
it is that which killed him.

But see! Dancers from every country suddenly appear before the Queen: a fiery Andalusian, a melancholy German maiden, a baya-dere from India with golden rings in her nostrils, all who have lived, all who have died for and through the dance. They spring up from the earth, alight from the trees, come from every direction.

When all have assembled, the Queen proposes the admission of Giselle, a maiden who has just died.

Her dancing will do honor to their fantastic corps de ballet. As the others watch, the Queen points her magic wand, bound round with verbena, toward the tomb.

Suddenly, from amidst the undergrowth, a slender figure springs up, straight and white and stiff as though still in its coffin. It is Giselle, awakened from the heavy, dreamless slumber of the dead in their damp shrouds.

Raised from the dead and still very numb, she takes a few tottering steps. But soon the fresh night air and the silvery moonlight restore her high spirits. Joyfully, she takes possession of space once again. How freely she breathes, her chest rid at last of the stone's dead weight. What happiness—to be light and free again, to soar at will, alighting here or there like a capricious butterfly!

Humbly, she approaches the Queen of the Wilis and kneels before her. A star is set upon her brow; two delicate little wings unfold quivering from her shoulders. Two little wings and two such feet—it is really too much!

The ceremony completed, the wilis prepare to teach their fantastic waltz to the young initiate. But their efforts are hardly needed; Giselle already knows it better than any of them.

Now, tardy travelers, take care! Do not pass the fatal clearing once midnight has struck, or your road may lead you to the bottom of the lake, down amid the muck and the reeds, with only the frogs for company.

At this very moment, a victim appears. The wretched Hilarion, haunted by remorse and led astray by a treacherous forest path, finds himself back where he started—the grave of Giselle.

The wilis grab at him. They push him on all sides, whirl him about, pass him down the line of dancers, from arm to arm, from hand to hand. His legs buckle under him—he struggles for breath; he begs brokenly for mercy.

No mercy! The waltzers of this world may be pitiless, but those of the next world are crueler still.

Hilarion is caught, released, then caught again. Every wili seeks a share in his destruction. And they are everywhere! Now there are ten—now twenty—now thirty of them! Into the water with you, Hilarion! You are weary, your feet are dragging. . . . Of what possible use is a tired dancer, except to be tossed into the lake?

At last, the ghostly little hands push the heavy, massive body over the edge of the bank. The water plashes, boils up; two or three circles spread, slowly dying, across the oily surface of the marsh.

Good night, Hilarion. Justice is done!

The leaves tremble; a hand parts the branches. Who dares approach this frightening spot at such an hour? It is Albrecht, maddened with grief, come to weep at Giselle's grave and to beg pardon of the beloved shade. For Albrecht did not wholly deceive Giselle, though he lied about his rank. His love was sincere and his words of love echoed the wishes of his heart.

Giselle, moved by Albrecht's tears, breathes a faint sigh—the sigh of a spirit. Albrecht whirls around to see two stars of azure twinkling in the foliage. They are her eyes—it is Giselle!

Oh pity, matchless vision, do not vanish! Let me look once more on that sweet face I thought to see again only in heaven. And he rushes forward with arms outstretched, but embraces only the reeds and lianas.

A white vapor crosses the somber forest thicket. Once again, it is Giselle. Hidden in a cluster of flowers, she plucks a few, touches them to her lips, and throws the flowers with her kisses to her love.

But the wilis, ogresses of the waltz, have sensed the presence of a fresh dancer. They rush in to claim their share of grisly pleasure.

Giselle clasps her hands in entreaty.

"Wicked ones!" she cries. "Leave me my Loys. Do not put him to death. Let him live to enjoy the soft light of heaven, to remember me and weep upon my tomb. It is so sweet to feel a warm tear penetrate beneath the earth, to feel it fall from a burning eye onto one's cold heart."

"No, no, no! Let him dance and let him die!"

"Do not listen to them, my Loys. Cling to the cross on my grave. Whatever you may see, whatever you may hear, do not leave it!

The cross is your refuge, it is your salvation. Its power can break
Myrtha's wand."

"True," says the Queen, with a commanding gesture. "My wand
loses its power before that cross. But you, Giselle, are subject to my
will. I order you to dance the most chaste and the most voluptuous
of dances, to look at him with your most tender glances, to smile
your most charming of deathly smiles. Albrecht will quit the cross
of his own accord."

49

Giselle, yielding despite herself to the powerful magic, obeys with steps that are slow and languorous. Her furtive glance searches the horizon . . . the night is passing. Surely the cock must crow soon and day must break. If only Albrecht will cling to his sanctuary, he will be saved. The unhappy shade tries to appear less beautiful, less seductive. Useless!

Now Myrtha forces Giselle to pour more energy into the dance. Giselle must obey for she is a wili, after all. The intoxication of the dance seizes her: she flies, she bounds, she whirls, and Loys, oblivious to his fate, leaps after her and follows her steps, happy to die in the arms of the beloved phantom.

The mad dance, brilliant and dizzying, seems to go on forever.
Albrecht pales. His breath comes in gasps. He is about to fall into
the treacherous waters when suddenly—

a far-off bell begins to strike the hour:

one, two, three, four o'clock.

A feeble bar of light takes shape in the clouds behind the hill; the
glimmer grows into a brightness. The wilis, frightened of the morning, scatter and reenter their hiding places in the hearts of the water
lilies, in the clefts of the rocks, and in the hollows of the trees.
Albrecht is saved.

Giselle sinks down onto the grass. The flowers enfold and close in over her, and her transparent body melts away like a vapor. Only her frail white hand still beckons in a last farewell to the love she must see no more. Then the hand, too, disappears. The earth has reclaimed its prey, never again to yield it up.

Albrecht tears frantically through the foliage, but he can see nothing. A single rose, plucked from the grave, is all that remains to Count Albrecht of the poor village girl. But it still breathes the chaste perfume of the soul of Giselle.

The curtain falls.

A Role for a Lifetime

I never prepared anything in my whole life as much as I did Giselle. It's a
role that grows with you, a role in which you can discover new aspects at
every stage of your career and your own personal development. It's also a
role that poses enormous technical and dramatic challenges; how you rise
to these challenges at different stages of your life adds of course to the fas-
cination of Giselle, both for the dancer and the audience.

Perhaps the most important aspect to be developed is the contrast between the two acts of *Giselle* — between the directness, the wonderful
joyousness of the first act, and the frozen gestures, the Romantic lithograph
effects of the second act.

In the first act, you dance with your whole body. There are no inhibi-
tions and you jump a great deal. The action is direct, open, and explicit.

At the beginning, you have all the blood going. Giselle is young, she's a
peasant girl, and she lives in the country. Giselle is the epitome of what one
hopes is freshness and innocence—but she is no aristocrat; she has good
red blood in her veins and she breathes good country air. She is like some
healthy, graceful young animal—therefore she jumps, she leaps, she em-
ploys free, full gestures. Only with Albrecht does Giselle show the inhibi-
tions you expect in a Romantic heroine.

To Albrecht, of course, Giselle is the embodiment of certain ideals—the freedom he cannot have, the carefree youth denied him, the innocence he cannot hope to possess. The Princess represents the call of duty. She's probably a very nice Princess, but she's his father's choice, and it's all very boring. But Giselle is his own discovery.

In the second act, the peasant girl has become the ideal Romantic woman—unattainable, very high *en pointe*, almost beyond reach.

Giselle is now a shadow. So she has to have that sort of extraordinary understanding that a shadow has acquired. Even though she might never have been the wife, she has already become the mother. All the aspects, all the stages in a woman's life are now reflected in her relationship with Albrecht: she can be the protective mother and the fiancée; she can be the mistress, the woman, the wife.

Giselle herself wears a long, mid-calf *tutu*, a costume I have worn in Balanchine ballets as well. It's wonderful to dance in, though it does change the emphasis in the presentation of your body. The feet become *essentially* important: Because the full line of the leg up to the hip does not show up very well owing to the long *tutu*, the footwork becomes the eloquent part of your legwork. You have to put your expression, so to speak, into your feet. You have to *present* them—they must be fleet, fast, very nicely pointed, caressing; you have to work with your feet literally as you would with your hands. I worked a tremendously long time on this important aspect of Giselle's vocabulary.

The ballet's second act makes far greater demands on the dancer and interpreter. The movements of the head, neck, arms, and feet are almost isolated, one from the other. You must establish a "weeping willow" quality, an enveloping quality as soft as mist. The wilis are nature spirits, after all. A walk must become a glide—as though you were walking on clouds. The arms are those of a creature of air and water: they are wet and heavy and soft. The jumps take on a different quality: Giselle is no longer the exuberant village girl; she is a spirit possessed and driven by an outside force. There must be no suggestion of the physical effort of dancing.

Of course the effect of complete effortlessness demands far greater technical control. The legs that propel you through the air as a wili must be just as strong as in Act I—even stronger, in fact. Passages calling for extreme lightness and fast footwork contrast with the great, slow *adagio* sections danced both with and without Albrecht. After the emotional wear and tear of the first act, you must somehow find your way to the nerve-defying control that permits you to do those slow-motion variations.

How, then, does the dancer reconcile two acts that are almost two separate ballets? Actually, both the poet and the choreographer provide a thread of continuity in the love of Giselle for Albrecht. In the first act, she is a young, innocent girl, in love for the first time and almost torn between her love for Albrecht and her love of the dance. The two are almost too much for one person, and therein lies the core of Giselle's tragedy. In the second act the love for Albrecht is idealized; it has become mature, selfless, conquering fear and death.

Of course it takes a poet's vocabulary to describe *Giselle* and that's why I so enjoyed translating Gautier's story. You cannot talk about the dance as you would talk of sports or politics; it requires a special language, and Gautier knew that language. He also knew the elements of the dance, having attended so many rehearsals and performances. He was one of the few initiates of the ballet—a kind of literary Degas.

I have danced a wide variety of roles, including the Swan Queen and the Sleeping Beauty. But Giselle is a very special kind of role: it gives you the chance literally to give all of yourself to it, and by the same token to discover how much you have to offer—in terms of the disappointments as well as the successes. Giselle gives you a chance to explore all your capacities—you have to be a complete dancer and a complete person. And that is what Giselle is all about.

Violette Verdy
New York   1970